DESPICABLE ME

MINION M™

2015 ANNUAL

Published 2014. Century Books Ltd.
Unit 1, Upside Station Building Solsbro Road,
Torquay, Devon, UK, TQ26FD

books@centumbooksltd.co.uk

All rights reserved. No part of this publication may be reproduced,
stored in a retrieval system, or transmitted in any form or by any
means, electronic, mechanical, photocopying, recording or otherwise,
without the prior written permission of the publisher

centum

£7.99

CONTENTS

DESPICABLE ME

MINION MADE

WELCOME

Hello,

I used to be one of the world's best super villains – pretty much ever! I even stole the moon! Yeah, that was me!

And after adopting Margo, Edith, and Agnes I thought I had hung up my Freeze Ray for good. But then, the Anti-Villain League begged me to join them, because they couldn't catch a cold without me. So now I'm a SPY! That's right baby, I'm back and cooler than ever...

But I need your help to solve the puzzles and find the hidden clues so I can crack the case.

If you are brave and cunning enough to enter a world of spies and super-villains, then open up and read on...

Gru

Gru

Gru is now a spy for a secret crime-fighting organisation, the AVL. He has loads of cool new weapons and gadgets to help him catch criminals! Guide Gru through the maze and collect his weapons along the way.

Status:

Margo, Edith & Agnes

Gru's three daughters, Margo, Edith and Agnes are intelligent, cheeky and very cute. Can you solve these clues about their favourite things and fill in the crossword puzzle? Use the hints to help you.

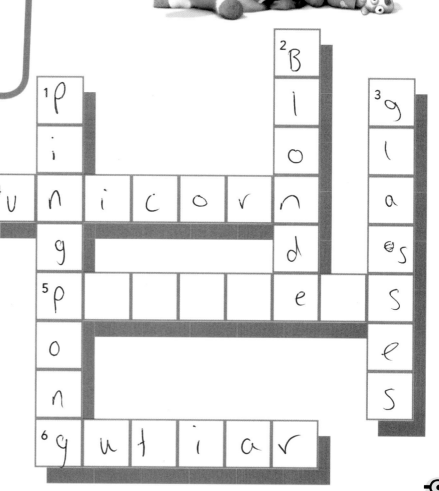

Down

1. What is Edith's favourite sport?
   Hint: ipgn npog

2. Edith's hair colour is . . .
   Hint: nedlob

3. Margo is the only one of Gru's daughters who wears . . .
   Hint: sesagls

Across

4. Agnes's favourite stuffed toy is a . . .
   Hint:

5. What did Agnes dress up as, for her birthday?
   Hint: siperncs

6. What musical instrument does Margo play?
   Hint: tguria

4. u n i c o r n

6. g u t i a r

Minion Hide & Seek Word Search

The Minions have hidden some words and names in this fun little word search, can you find all 10 hidden in amongst this maze of letters, tick them off in the box below as you go…

```
A R O N B P G P A R A D I S E
R L K A I E R O L L W A Q D R
Y P P A H X Z C B T I G I H Y
A G N E S F S S U Y T T S O V
M A R A M E O A L O H L E V M
S S J Y D V W O N U A O U O S
N H N B L T T O D R M I K C N
P O B L Y L M E E C T Y Z F T
E P E W M A A K E T O H O E K
K S A R O E R M N O Q U L R H
A A U T Y P G O T R N P R E J
C T T K P F O L D T L O G T G
P F O R N E T I A S K P P D V
U O F R V D N I B L A O R A E
C O U E A T N A R U A T S E R
```

1. PARADISE ☑
2. MALL ☑
3. FOUNTAIN ☑
4. SHOPS ☑
5. FOOD COURT ☑
6. MARGO ☑
7. EDITH ☑
8. AGNES ☑
9. CUPCAKE ☑
10. RESTAURANT ☑

REMEMBER! The words could be hiding down, across, diagonally or backwards.

Gru's wacky scientist, Dr. Nefario, loves to create weird and wonderful inventions. Help him to shoot the Evil Minion in the grid below with his Jam Blaster! Draw a path from the start square to the Minion at the bottom. You can only go in the direction that Dr. Nefario is pointing at.

Dr. Nefario

Start

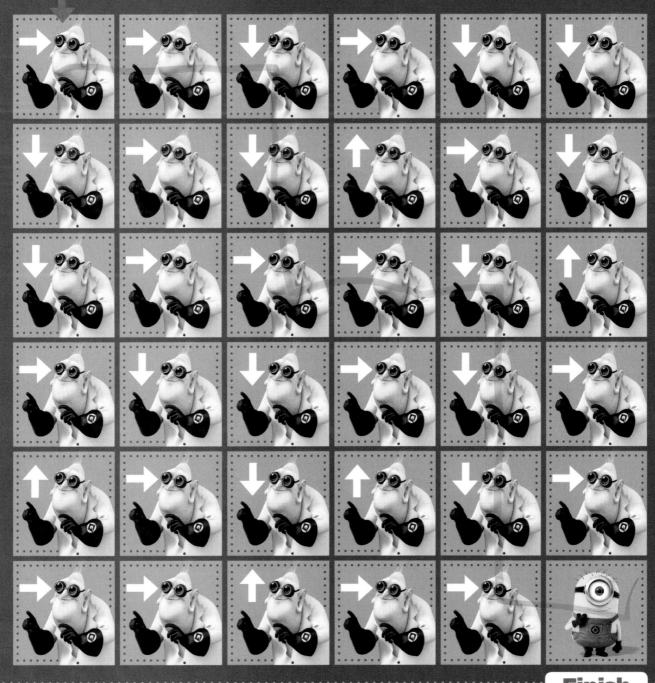

Finish

9

Lucy

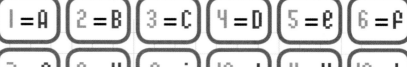

1 = A	2 = B	3 = C	4 = D	5 = e	6 = F
7 = g	8 = H	9 = i	10 = J	11 = K	12 = L
13 = M	14 = N	15 = O	16 = P	17 = Q	
18 = R	19 = S	20 = T	21 = U	22 = V	
23 = W	24 = X	25 = Y	26 = Z		

Lucy's secret message:

[20][15][16]
[19][5][3][18][5][20] :
[2][18][5][1][11] - [9][14]
[20][15][14][9][7][8][20]

Top secret
break in
Tonight

Write your cracked code here:

[20][15][16] [2][12][1][8]
[2][12][1][8]
[2][12][1][8]

Agent Lucy Wilde is Gru's new spy partner. She loves all sorts of spy work, especially writing secret messages! Can you decipher this message using the code cracker?

10

El Macho

El Macho is one of the most ruthless and dangerous villains of all time. Gru needs to follow him into his secret lair.
Can you help? Study the entry light pattern opposite. Then find it five times in the grid.

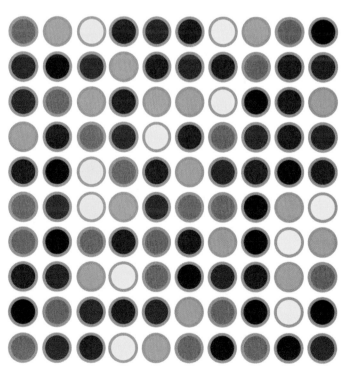

REMEMBER!
The light pattern could be hiding down, across or diagonally.

11

Minions

Some of Gru's loyal, yellow Minions have been injected with the PX-41 serum and they are starting to mutate! Study the Minions carefully and decide which ones are turning evil.

Minions

Gru is the leader of a whole army of yellow gibberish-speaking Minions. They love causing chaos! Take a look at these two pictures of the cheeky chaps. At first they look the same, but ten things are different between them. Can you spot them all? Tick each yellow Minion below as you spot each difference!

Gru was once one of the world's greatest super-villains. He and his Minions even stole the moon! But then he adopted Margo, Edith and Agnes. Now he takes his responsibilities as a dad very seriously, so he gave up his life of crime.

But there is a new mastermind criminal on the loose! Someone has used a gigantic magnetic hover-ship to steal a top-secret formula from a lab in the Arctic Circle.

In a secret spy bunker, a group of government agents watches footage of the lab theft.

"We're still no closer to cracking this," announces a round man with a posh English accent, " - bring him in!"

It is Agnes's sixth birthday and Gru is getting organised.
He grabs a scary looking gun, pulls the trigger and . . . POP!
A unicorn balloon appears from the end. Finally, the backyard
is ready. There are streamers, balloons and a huge bouncy castle.

Soon the party is in full swing. Agnes and her friends are
dressed as princesses. Edith shows off her martial arts and
Margo protects children from Kyle who wears a dragon costume!

"What do you mean she's not coming?" Gru yells into his mobile phone. "I am begging you!" he pleads. "I have a backyard full of little girls who are counting on a visit from a fairy princess!"

But the person on the other end of the phone still says no.

Gru lowers his voice to a growl. "I hope you can sleep at night, you crusher of little girls' dreams!"

Gru has no idea what to do. Suddenly an idea pings into his head. He goes to the house.

A minute later, Agnes screams, "The fairy princess! Look!" She points to the sky.

Dangling in the air is Gru! Dressed in a puffy pink dress and a curly wig.

A group of his Minions struggle to lower him from the roof, but they get distracted by a balloon and accidentally drop him. Gru smashes into the house and crashes to the ground.

"It is I, Gru. . .zinkerbell! The most magical fairy princess of all!" Gru announces in a high-pitched voice. "I am here to wish Princess Agnes a very happy birthday!" Agnes beams with joy.

"OK, time for cake!" cries Gru.

The other children cheer and run to the table, but Agnes approaches Gru.

"Thank you, Gru-zinkerbell. You're the best fairy princess ever!" Then she turns and whispers, "I know it's really you, Gru. I'm just pretending for the other kids."

Jillian, an annoying mother at the party, comes over to pester Gru.

"Sooo . . ." she begins. "My friend, Natalie is recently single and-"

"No, no, no," Gru replies. He realises that she wants to send him on a date.

Jillian carries on, "Come on, she's a riot. Looks aren't that important to her . . . " Gru sprays her with the garden hose. "Sorry, I did not see you there." Then he sprays her again. "Or there . . ." He chuckles to himself and walks off.

As dusk falls, Gru takes Kyle outside.

"Mr Gru?" says a stranger's voice from behind him.

He spins around to see a tall, sharply-dressed, redheaded woman.

"Hi. Agent Lucy Wilde of the Anti-Villain League . . . You're going to have to come with me."

"Oh, sorry, I - FREEZE RAY!" Gru pulls out his weapon and shoots ice at Lucy.
Just as quickly, she fires a mini-flamethrower, which instantly melts the ice.
"You know, you really should announce your weapons after you fire them, Mr. Gru," Lucy says. "For example . . ."
She whips out a tube of lipstick and points it at Gru. Two tiny darts hit him in the chest - Zzzap!
Gru's body shakes and dances in every direction before he finally collapses.
" . . .Lipstick Zapper!" Lucy cries.

After a lot of effort, Lucy loads Gru into the boot of her car.
Just as she is about to pull away, two of Gru's Minions, Tom and Stuart, see what is happening and run after Lucy's car. She spots the two minions following her and zaps them too.

Lucy drives through town and then right off the pier - SPLASH! Her car transforms into an underwater vehicle and glides through the water. Soon, they arrive at an enormous submarine.

Inside, Lucy ejects a groggy Gru from the boot.

"Good evening, Mr. Gru, " says the same round man from earlier with the very posh English accent. "My name is Silas Ramsbottom. And we . . . "he gestures around a huge room, full of people, "are the Anti-Villain League."

Gru looks at him, more confused than ever. Silas explains, "It's an ultra-secret organisation dedicated to fighting crime on a global scale. Rob a bank? We're not interested. But if you want to melt the polar ice caps? Or even steal the moon? Then we notice."

"First of all, you've got no proof I did that," Gru objects. "And after I did do that, I put it back!"

Lucy takes over the presentation. "Recently an entire top secret lab disappeared from the Arctic Circle. Just whoosh! Gone," she explains.

They show Gru the film of the magnetic ship stealing the laboratory. Then it changes to show a cute, fluffy bunny undergoing tests in a lab.

"The lab was devoted to experiments involving PX-41, a transmutation serum," Lucy continues.

Onscreen, the bunny is injected with a purple liquid. It quickly transforms into a hideous, purple, monster bunny! It goes crazy and attacks the scientists.

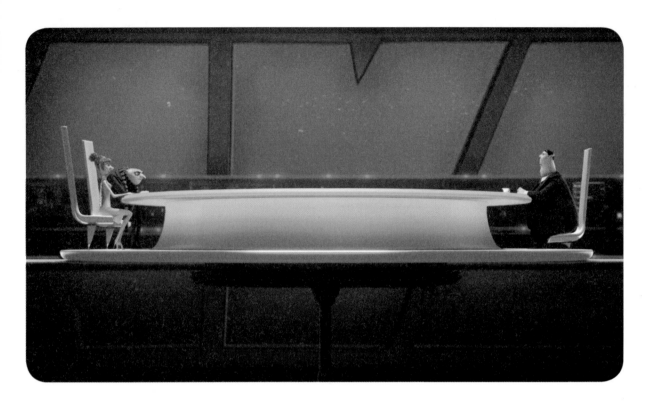

"As you can see, in the wrong hands, the PX-41 serum could be the most devastating weapon on earth!" Silas tells Gru. "We found traces of it in the Paradise Mall."

"A mall?" Gru repeats doubtfully.

"We believe that one of the shop owners is a master criminal. That's where you come in," Silas says to Gru. "As an ex-villain, you know how a villain thinks, how he acts."

PX41

Lucy explains the plan - "We want to set you up, undercover, at a shop in the mall-"

Gru shakes his head. "No! I am a father now. And, a legitimate businessman. I am developing a line of delicious jams and jellies."

"Jams and jellies?" repeats Silas sarcastically.

"Oh, attitude!" Gru cries and storms out. Lucy runs after him.

"I probably shouldn't be saying this," she begins, "but your work as a villain was kind of amazing. So if you ever want to get back to doing something awesome, give us a call." As she goes, she hands Gru her business card.

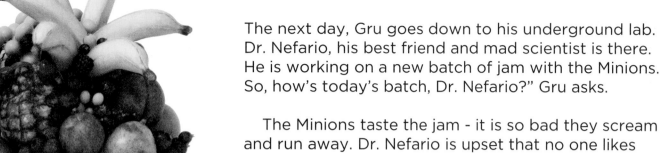

The next day, Gru goes down to his underground lab. Dr. Nefario, his best friend and mad scientist is there. He is working on a new batch of jam with the Minions. So, how's today's batch, Dr. Nefario?" Gru asks.

The Minions taste the jam - it is so bad they scream and run away. Dr. Nefario is upset that no one likes his creations.

"Just because everybody hates it, doesn't mean it's not good," Gru says, trying to brighten his mood.

"Listen, Gru," sighs Dr. Nefario. "There's something I've been meaning to talk to you about."

Gru senses something is up. "What's wrong?"

"I miss being evil," admits Dr. Nefario. "Sinister plots, large-scale crimes . . . it's what I live for! I mean, don't you think there's more to our future than jam?"

"Well, I'm also considering a line of chutneys . . ."

Dr. Nefario is disappointed. "Um . . . the thing is, Gru, I've had an offer of employment elsewhere."

Gru stares at his friend. He can't believe he wants to leave him. Finally he answers, "Let us give you the proper send-off, the twenty-one Fart Gun salute."

Dr. Nefario sits on his scooter. Gru calls the Minions to line up. Seven of them hold Fart Guns and fire three times. .

Dr. Nefario's eyes begin to water, and not just from the smell. He comments, "Uh, I counted twenty-two." Gru looks down at Dave who blushes.

"Farewell, my friends! I miss you already!" calls Dr. Nefario as he slowly flies his hover-scooter away from Gru's underground lab.

Gru watches him go, sad that his oldest friend is leaving him. He pulls out Lucy Wilde's business card from his pocket and makes a decision.

That night, Tom dressed as a French Maid vacuums the house. He hears the doorbell and answers the door. A bag is thrown over his head and a mystery person carries him off. The Minion abductions have begun . . .

Agnes, Edith and Margo are playing on Gru's laptop when he walks in.

"I have an announcement to make," he says proudly. "I have a new job. I have been recruited by a top secret agency to go undercover and save the world!"

"You're going to be a spy?" Edith exclaims.

"That's right, baby! With gadgets and weapons and cool cars . . . the whole deal." He puts on a pair of sunglasses and strikes a cool spy pose.

The next day, Gru starts work at Paradise Mall. He steps inside his cupcake shop, Bake My Day. This shop will be his cover while he spies on the other shop owners and tries to find the master criminal hidden amongst them.

He looks around the shop and sees . . . Lucy!

"Why are you here?" Gru demands.

"On an assignment from Silas," explains Lucy. "I'm your new partner. Yay!"

"What? No 'yay'! Ramsbottom didn't say anything about a partner," Gru complains.

Lucy shrugs. "Well, seems that because of your chequered past, everyone else refused to work with you. I'm new, so I kind of have to do what they tell me, anyway."

Lucy and Gru get to work. They pull down the lampshade mini-command centre and operate a hidden spy-camera on the front of the shop.

"OK, first suspect - Hedda Blumentoft, proprietor of Mum's the Word flower shop." Onscreen they see an innocent looking lady.

"No, not her," replies Gru.

Lucy moves the camera to the next suspect. They see a short Asian man wearing a silly blonde wig.

"Next," announces Lucy, "Floyd Eagle-san, owner of Eagle Hair Club."

"His only crime is that wig, right?" Gru jokes. Suddenly he becomes frustrated. "Are we looking at the same people? Because there is no way they are villains!"

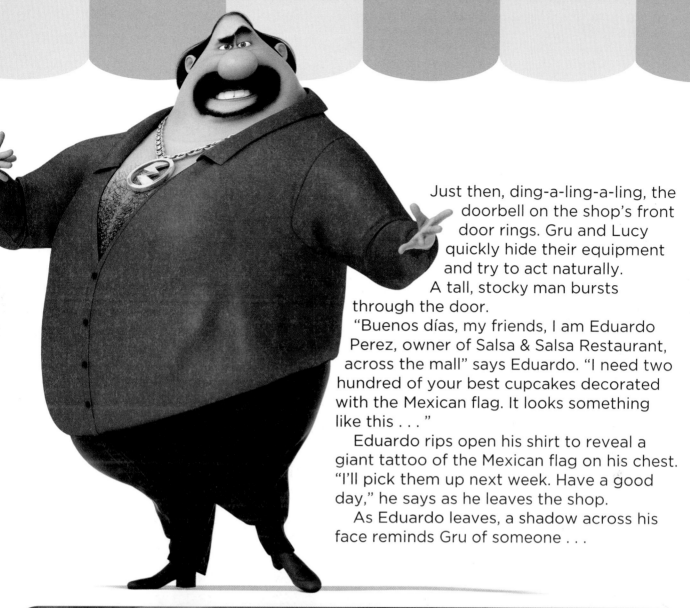

Just then, ding-a-ling-a-ling, the doorbell on the shop's front door rings. Gru and Lucy quickly hide their equipment and try to act naturally.

A tall, stocky man bursts through the door.

"Buenos días, my friends, I am Eduardo Perez, owner of Salsa & Salsa Restaurant, across the mall" says Eduardo. "I need two hundred of your best cupcakes decorated with the Mexican flag. It looks something like this . . . "

Eduardo rips open his shirt to reveal a giant tattoo of the Mexican flag on his chest. "I'll pick them up next week. Have a good day," he says as he leaves the shop.

As Eduardo leaves, a shadow across his face reminds Gru of someone . . .

"El Macho," Gru gasps.

"What?" says Lucy.

"That guy looks exactly like a villain named El Macho, from about twenty years ago," explains Gru. "He was ruthless, dangerous and as the name implies, very macho."

Gru tells Lucy the legend of El Macho. How he performed daring heists with his bare hands.

"But sadly, like all the greats, El Macho was gone too soon," Gru continues. "He died in the most macho way possible - riding a shark with two hundred and fifty pounds of dynamite strapped to his chest into the mouth of an active volcano!"

"Sounds like El Macho is pretty dead!" Lucy says.

"No, they never found the body. Only a pile of singed chest hair." He thinks about Eduardo. "But that face! It has got to be El Macho."

Lucy thinks. "I say we break into his restaurant tonight!"

That night, Gru tucks the girls into bed before the big break-in.

"So, hugs, kisses, goodnight, sleep tight, don't let the bedbugs blah-blah-blah . . ." he hurriedly mumbles.

He turns to leave but Agnes is in his way.

"You said you'd help me practise my part for the Mother's Day show!" she says.

Gru looks down at Agnes's puppy dog eyes.

"Fine, fine. Let me hear it - quickly," he grumbles.

Agnes immediately begins to recite her part.

"She kisses my boo-boos.
She braids my hair.
My mother is beyond compare.
We love you mothers, everywhere!"

Unfortunately, when Agnes says the poem, she sounds like a robot. Gru forces a smile.

"Wow. That was something else! Let's try it one more time, but a teensy bit less like a zombie, OK?" he says encouragingly.

"I don't think I should do this," she announces glumly.

"What do you mean? Why not?" asks Gru.

"I don't have a mum," sniffles Agnes.

Gru tries to cheer her up. "You don't need one to do the show, " he replies. "Just use your imagination."

"You mean pretend I have a mum?" Agnes asks.

"Yes," Gru replies. "Can you do that?"

"Yeah! I do that all the time," she says and runs off to bed.

After Gru leaves the house, something strange happens. In the backyard, a light beams down from the sky. Two Minions are sucked up into the air. These Minions have been abducted too!

At the Paradise Mall, all the shops are closed. The entire building is empty. Gru and Lucy emerge from their hiding place beneath the floorboards. They sneak up to the door of Eduardo's restaurant and break inside. Gru heads to the kitchen.

"Wait!" shouts Lucy. "You never know what sort of booby traps this guy could have set."

"It's a restaurant," Gru points out, annoyed. "There are no booby traps!"

He takes a step forward and kicks a tripwire attached to a bell. Ding-a-ling.

"Ha, booby!" cries Lucy triumphantly. Then the kitchen door creaks open to reveal . . . a chicken!

Gru laughs. "Some guard dog," he mocks. Suddenly, the chicken leaps into the air. It lands on Gru and starts pecking his bald head.

"Ahhhh! Get it off me! Get it off me!" Gru yelps.
Lucy points her watch at the angry bird. She presses a button and foam squirts over the chicken. It instantly hardens and the bird is trapped.

In the kitchen, Lucy pulls out a high-tech scanning device.

"I'm getting extremely high traces of tortilla," she whispers to Gru. He rolls his eyes.

Lucy pulls out a pair of X-ray goggles and hands them to Gru. He inspects the kitchen through the goggles and sees something behind a painting on the wall. It's a safe - with a canister inside!

"I knew it!" shouts Gru triumphantly. "The PX-41 serum is in here!" He yanks the painting off the wall and breaks open the safe.

Inside, the mysterious metal canister is surrounded by mist. Gru turns around to reveal a label that reads, 'Eduardo's Secret Salsa Recipe.' Gru opens it and sniffs. He dips in his finger and licks it!

"Salsa?" he says confused.

Meanwhile, Eduardo returns to the restaurant. He spots his bird encased in the hardened foam.

"Pollito!" Eduardo cries. "Who would do this to a sweet little chicken?"

"Bawk!" squawks Pollito.
Eduardo turns towards the kitchen, "I know you're in there!"

"He's coming!" cries Lucy.

Gru pulls a laser cutter from his pocket and aims it at the ceiling. The laser fires and cuts a hole. Eduardo shoves open the kitchen door, ready for battle. But all he sees is a pair of legs disappear through the ceiling.

"Stop!" he bellows.

Lucy shoots him in the face with more foam from her watch. Eduardo wails in pain.

A few seconds later . . . Crash! The Minions smash Lucy's car through the glass doors of the mall. Gru and Lucy jump into the car just as Eduardo runs from the restaurant.

Lucy hits a button. The car transforms into a jet. They fly off into the night sky . . .

The next day at the mall, Gru and Lucy look for their next possible suspect. They hide in rubbish bins to disguise themselves as they carry out surveillance of the area.

"There he is - suspect number eight, Floyd Eagle-san."

Gru recognises him and sighs. "I told you, that's not the guy."

Lucy doesn't believe him. "See if you can get closer. Go!" she insists.

Gru stands up in the rubbish bin. He makes his way over to Floyd. But he doesn't see the escalator. He trips and falls, landing at the bottom with a thud. The bin pops off his head. Standing above him, Gru sees Margo, Edith and Agnes.

"Girls!" cries Gru. "What are you doing here?"

"We thought we'd come and visit you at work," Margo explains. "So . . . you're saving the world in a rubbish bin?"

Gru doesn't have chance to answer because Lucy walks over to join them.

Agnes stares at Lucy - she looks like a perfect mother.

"Are you single?" Agnes blurts out. Lucy is shocked. "Oh . . . goodness." This is awkward!

"Hey! I have an idea! Why don't you girls go and explore the mall?" says Gru.

"Are you going to marry Lucy?" asks Agnes.

What! No, she is just my partner. She works with me," he replies. "Now go and have fun," he says pointing to the mall.

Outside Gru's house, an ice cream truck makes it way down the road. A mob of Minions bursts through the front door and chases it, shouting, "Gelato! Gelato!"

Suddenly, the metal ice cream cone on top of the van opens and begins to suck the Minions into it!

After shopping, Margo, Edith and Agnes sit by the fountain in Paradise Mall. Margo is texting when something catches her eye - a boy!

He looks cool and is wearing a black leather jacket. He strolls behind the fountain and disappears. Margo springs up to search for the mystery boy.

She slips! The boy appears as if from nowhere and catches her. She gazes up at him as if she's in a love story.

"I'm Antonio," he whispers.

"I'm Margo," she replies nervously.

"I was just going to get a cookie," Antonio continues. "Care to join me?"

Antonio takes Margo's hand and leads her towards Salsa & Salsa Restaurant. Agnes and Edith stare after their sister.

Edith makes a face. "Ewww!" Agnes cries, "We've got to tell Gru!"

Agnes and Edith stare after their sister. Edith makes a face. "Ewww!" Agnes cries, "We've got to tell Gru!"

Across the mall, Gru is about to enter Eagle Hair Club. He adjusts a device on his belt buckle that scans for traces of PX-41. Lucy is monitoring from the cupcake shop. She talks to Gru through a tiny earpiece he is wearing.

As Gru steps inside, a large chair shaped like an eagle spins around. Sitting in the chair is Floyd Eagle-san, looking sinister.

"It's about time you showed up, Mr. Gru," growls Floyd.

Gru is stunned. "You know my name?" he stutters.

"When someone who is folically-challenged moves into the mall, I make it my business to know all about them," replies Floyd.

Back in the cupcake shop, Lucy monitors the serum-tracking device. "Nothing so far," she whispers to Gru through his earpiece. "I think you need to move around."

Gru moves to a shelf stacked with wigs. The device makes a loud noise.

"Behind that wall!" she yells at Gru.

He moves the wigs aside and tries to see what's behind the wall. Floyd picks up one of the wigs.

"These are my trial wigs," Floyd says to Gru. "You should take one. I promise that this wig will transform you from ugly to irresistible."

Gru gets distracted. He stares at the wig. He is about to respond, when Edith and Agnes burst in.

"Margo has a boyfriend!" squeals Agnes.

"And they're on a date!" Edith adds.
Gru is shocked. His mouth falls open. "Date? Boyfriend? What?"

Still holding the wig, he races through the mall to Salsa & Salsa Restaurant.

Antonio and Margo sit at the back of the restaurant and stare at each other.

"My dream is to one day play video games for a living," Antonio says to Margo.

Gru interrupts the romantic scene, trying to stay calm Before Gru can say anything Salsa music begins to play in the restaurant. A curtain opens to reveal - Eduardo!

Eduardo walks over to Gru and gives him a hug.

"So good to see you again, mi compadre!" says Eduardo.

Antonio smiles at Gru. "I see you have already met my father," he says.

"Father?" exclaims Gru.

"Si!" replies Eduardo. "Crazy, small world we live in, eh?"

Gru looks down to see Eduardo's chicken glaring at him. Gru tries to stroke it, but Pollito lunges at him.

"Oh, I'm sorry," cries Eduardo. "He had a rough night."

Eduardo looks at Antonio and Margo. "Young love. It's beautiful, no?" he sighs.

"No!" Gru yells. "They're not in love. They hardly know each other."

"You are right," cries Eduardo. "They must get to know each other better. Antonio, why don't you invite your girlfriend and her family to our Cinco de Mayo party?"

"No-" Gru begins.

"Si!" squeal the girls.

Gru glares at Antonio - with a look that could kill!

Meanwhile, on a beautiful, exotic, mystery beach, the Minions are having a party! This is where all the abducted Minions have been taken. But, the Minions don't know that this party is happening inside a giant fish tank. And they are being watched . . .

That night at the AVL headquarters, Gru and Lucy meet with Silas.

"El Macho?" says Silas, sounding confused. "Hadn't we eliminated him as a suspect? After the whole salsa incident?"

"Yes, but there has been a new development," protests Gru. "I'm telling you this is the guy. You need to arrest him immediately. And his deviously charming son!"

Silas shakes his head. "But I don't really see any evidence for-"

"Evidence, schmevidence," Gru butts in. "The kid gives me the creeps!"

Silas stares at Gru and wonders if he made the right decision to hire him.
Lucy tries to help the situation. "On a less crazy side of things, uh, Gru discovered traces of the serum at Eagle Hair Club."

"But it's not him. It's El Macho!" shouts Gru. "And I will prove it!"

Back home, Gru searches for articles about El Macho on his laptop. The doorbell rings - Ding-Dong!

"Gru, it's Jillian," a voice calls through the door.

Gru's eyes widen with fear.

"I have my friend Shannon here with me!" continues Jillian. "I was thinking you two could get some grub."

Gru starts to panic. Agnes skips into the room.

"Agnes, quick, tell Jillian I'm not here!" he whispers to her.

"Gru's not here," she calls to the door.

"Are you sure?" Jillian asks.

"Yes. He just told me!" replies Agnes proudly. Jillian sees through the lie. "I know you're in there, Gru. There's no getting out of this!" she yells.

Just then, Kyle runs over with the wig from Floyd Eagle-san in his mouth. Gru looks down at him and sighs, knowing what he has to do.

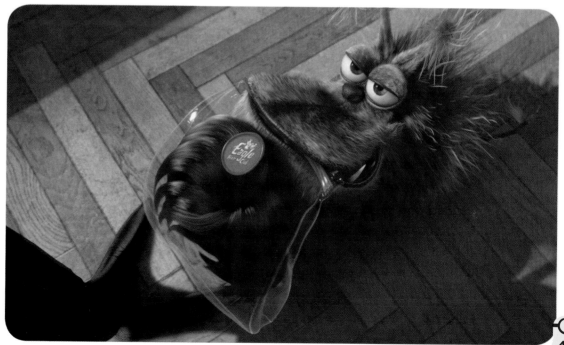

Gru and his date, Shannon, sit in the restaurant. He is now wearing the terrible wig on his head.

"I was nervous about tonight," begins Shannon. "I mean, there's just so many phonies out there."

Gru laughs nervously and hopes Shannon won't notice that he is wearing a wig.

Just then, Lucy walks in to the restaurant to pick up a take-away. Gru doesn't see her, but she sees Gru.
Lucy presses a button on her watch and it transforms into a high-tech listening device. Now she can hear Gru and Shannon talking.

"Your accent is so exotic," Shannon says to Gru.

"Thank you," Gru replies, smiling.

"I know someone who can fix that for you," Shannon blurts out.

Gru is embarrassed and starts to sweat.

"Is it hot in here?" he asks and wipes his brow. He accidently moves the wig. Shannon stares at Gru's hair.

"Are you wearing a wig?" Shannon demands.

"You're a phony. I'm going to rip that thing off you're head and show everyone what a bald-headed phony you are!" She reaches across the table for the wig.

Lucy has heard enough. "I don't think so, Miss Lady!" she whispers.

Lucy pushes another button on her watch. A mini-dart fires into Shannon's bottom. Shannon collapses and Gru is saved.

"Hey, Gru," calls Lucy as she walks over to him. He quickly pulls off the wig and tries to act casual.

"Hello, Lucy. How you doin'?"

"Wow. Your date is out for the count. Like she's been hit with a moose tranquiliser," she says with a wink.

Gru realises what Lucy did for him. He is impressed and grateful. "Well, thank you," he says with a smile.

Together they carry Shannon to the car and take her home.

At Shannon's house, they sit on the front step and rest.

"Well, you just had the worst date ever," Lucy tells Gru.

"Tell me about it," he groans. "Don't worry, it can only get better from here," she says. "But if it doesn't, you can always borrow my dart gun. Well, good night, partner."

Gru smiles. The word partner doesn't seem so bad now. He stares after Lucy. Something is happening. Could it be? Gru is in love.

The next day Gru skips to work, beaming. He's a new Gru!
At the mall, Gru dances his way to the cupcake shop. But everything comes to a stop when he sees that Eagle Hair Club is closed.

Gru spots Silas and some AVL agents walking from Eagle Hair Club.

"Mr. Ramsbottom?" Gru says to Silas. "What are you doing here?"

"We got Floyd Eagle-san!" Silas replies. "Our agents located a secret room in his shop last night and discovered traces of the PX-41 serum. So," Silas continues, "You're free to go back to your jam business. Agent Wilde is transferring to our Australian branch."

"Australia?" Gru says, shocked.
Lucy approaches from the shop.

"You're going to Australia?" Gru asks her.
"It's not definite yet," she says awkwardly.

"Well . . . good luck," says Gru, trying to hide his disappointment.

"Oh, I wanted to give you this," Lucy says. She takes out her Lipstick Zapper and hands it to Gru. "It's a memento of the first time we met . . ."

Gru is still too scared to ask her out. He watches Lucy walk away . . .

Just off Minion beach, Kevin floats happily in an inner tube. A hidden person watching in the control room pulls a lever. A whirlpool sucks the Minion down a tube and he lands on a chair.

A syringe full of purple PX-41 serum injects him in the neck. Suddenly, he transforms into a furry, purple, Evil Minion!

Gru is still trying not to think about Lucy. He drives Margo, Edith and Agnes to Eduardo's house. The Cinco de Mayo party is in full swing.

Gru turns and sees Margo holding hands with Antonio. They are face-to-face, almost close enough to kiss.

"Argh!" cries Gru. He picks up Antonio and places him far away from Margo.

"There must be the standard six feet of space between you and boys," he tells Margo. "Especially this boy!"

Antonio laughs. "You are a funny man. There are no rules, it's Cinco de Mayo!" He grabs Margo's hand and takes her to dance.

Meanwhile, Lucy sits on the aeroplane to Australia, feeling sad. Suddenly, she realises she is making the wrong decision.

She runs to the exit door of the plane and flings it open. Lucy jumps out of the plane and falls through the air.

She pulls a cord and her handbag turns into a hang-glider. She sails through the air on her way back to Gru.

Gru finds a quiet corner to sit down. He takes out the Lipstick Zapper and stares at it, remembering Lucy.

Just then, he notices Eduardo suspiciously sneak through a side door.
Gru follows him.

Gru peers through a crack and sees Eduardo standing in the middle of a secret room.

The floor is a series of different coloured tiles. He watches as Eduardo dances across them and plays a tune.

On the last note, a large Mexican statue's mouth opens. Eduardo walks through and into a lift.

Now it's Gru's turn. He steps onto the dance floor and tries to remember Eduardo's steps. He hits the wrong tile and activates a booby trap - an axe flies towards Gru's head.

After several failed attempts, he plays the correct tune. Gru steps into the lift
and descends to the secret lair . . .

The deeper the lift goes, the more nervous Gru becomes. The doors open and reveal a massive Evil den.

The magnetic ship from the laboratory heist is there!

Gru sees Eduardo wearing El Macho's wrestling outfit.

"I knew it!" shouts Gru. "You're El Macho. I knew you weren't dead."

"Of course not," agrees El Macho. "I merely faked my death. But now it's time to make my spectacular return to Evil! Doctor, it's time we showed Gru what we're up to."

He gestures to the lab, where Gru sees . . . Dr. Nefario!

Dr. Nefario pulls a lever. Kevin, one of Gru's Minions, rises through the floor. But it's an Evil purple version of Kevin.

"Kevin?" Gru whispers.

"He's not Kevin anymore," explains El Macho. "He's an indestructible, mindless killing machine. Watch!"

El Macho presses a button. A machine gun fires hundreds of bullets at Evil Kevin. But he's unhurt! Next, a flamethrower shoots fire at him. Still he is unharmed. He eats an axe, swallows a police car. He even eats an atomic bomb.

Gru is stunned.

"Impressive?" El Macho says proudly. "Here's the best part . . ."

He turns on the lights in the lab. It is full of cages containing Evil Minions.

"Soon I will unleash them onto the world," continues El Macho. "We can do it together. We would be unstoppable! Are you in?"

"Yeah, probably," mumbles Gru, realising how much danger he is in. "I mean yes. Yes! Of course." Gru needs to escape.

"Do you hear that? It sounds like Agnes calling me from the surface . . ." he jumps into the lift.

El Macho stares after him. "You know what? I am not so convinced that he is in."

He sets Evil Kevin free and sends him after Gru.

On the surface, Gru grabs Edith and Agnes. "We need to go home now!" he tells them.

Margo is sitting at a table alone. "Come on, we're leaving!" cries Gru.

Then he notices she is upset. "What's wrong?" he asks.

Margo sniffles and points to Antonio dancing with another girl. "I hate boys," she tells him.

Gru zaps Antonio with his Freeze Ray.

Their car drives away, just as Lucy lands with her hang-glider.

She runs into the party to look for Gru.

As she walks in, Pollito, the chicken, sees her and charges. She prepares to defend herself and her bag falls to the ground. Pollito pecks at it.

El Macho, dressed as Eduardo again, sees Pollito pecking Lucy's purse and picks him up "I apologise," he says. "The same thing happened the other day with . . . Gru . . ." He suddenly realises who she is.

"Speaking of Gru, have you seen him?" Lucy asks.

"You two are close, no?" replies El Macho.

"Did he say that?" she asks hopefully.

El Macho smiles. "It's more what he didn't say . . . for instance, he never mentioned that you were both working for the Anti-Villain League!"

He turns Pollito around. Lucy's AVL badge is in the chicken's beak!

El Macho puts his hand on her shoulder.

"You're coming with me," he growls.

In Gru's house, a video call flashes on the TV. He presses a button and Dr. Nefario appears onscreen.

"Gru! El Macho's on to you," Dr. Nefario cries. "He knows you work for the AVL. And he's got your partner!"

"Lucy?" Gru gasps. He turns to his Minions. "Let's go."

Later that day, Margo and Agnes hear a noise outside the house.

"What was that?" Agnes asks. She grabs her stuffed unicorn.

Margo walks towards the window when – SMASH! Evil Kevin crashes through the window.

"Blaaarrghhh!" he yells and charges towards them.

Margo and Agnes run for the lift. It drops just in time, leaving Evil Kevin to smash into the doors.

They run to the lab and shut the big steel door behind them. Phew! Nothing can get to them in Gru's reinforced lair.

Crunch . . . crunch . . .crunch!

Evil Kevin eats his way through the ceiling! They're doomed . . .

At that moment, a needle is injected into Evil Kevin. He falls over and begins to smoke and bubble.

When he sits up, he is a normal yellow Minion. Margo looks up to see who is holding the needle . . . it's Dr. Nefario!

"The antidote!" he says proudly and holds up a vial of yellow liquid.

He steps over to a vat of jam and pours the antidote into it.

"Let's put this horrible jam to good use," he grins.

In the meantime, Gru is led to El Macho's house by Dave and Stuart, painted purple to look like Evil Minions. He is handcuffed and held at spear point.
It's all part of Gru's plan to rescue Lucy.

They have a long walk to the house, past hundreds of suspicious Evil Minions. One of them makes a slobbery raspberry at Dave. He gets covered in sticky purple Minion slobber. When he rubs it off, the purple paint comes off, too!

They're exposed! The Evil Minions have their teeth bared and are ready to chomp.

"Run!" Gru yells. They scramble up to the roof.

Just as they are about to get eaten, Gru's ship appears with Dr. Nefario in the pilot's seat. This ship has been turned into a jam-dispensing weapon.

It opens fire on the Evil purple Minions. One by one, they transform back into yellow Minions.

Gru jumps into the ship. "Now let's get El Macho," says Gru.

"You got it!" says a girl's voice. Gru looks up to see Margo, Edith and Agnes on board the ship, holding jam blasters.

On the ground, El Macho watches in horror as his Evil Minion army is being transformed back to lots of normal Minions. Gru leaps from the ship to where El Macho is standing.

"It's over," he tells El Macho. "You've lost. Now where's Lucy?"

El Macho points to a rocket. Lucy is strapped to it, tied to a shark with 250 pounds of dynamite on its back!

El Macho holds a remote. "One push of this button and I send that rocket straight into a volcano," he growls.

Dave Minion knocks the remote out of El Macho's hand. It flies over the edge of the roof and lands on the ground below.

El Macho turns to Gru, "We could have ruled the world together. But now - you're gonna die!"

He pulls out a vial of PX-41 and drinks it!

He twitches, grows taller and hairier and turns purple! Gru gasps in horror at El Macho the monster.

Gru jumps to avoid El Macho's fists and falls backward off the roof. El Macho jumps too, ready to crush him.

Gru remembers Lucy's Lipstick Zapper.

He fires it at El Macho. "!"
he shouts.

A jolt of electricity shoots through El Macho's body. He shakes and collapses on the floor.

Dr. Nefario holds a blaster to El Macho's face.

"I am not afraid of your Jam guns,"
El Macho growls.

"Oh, this ain't a Jam gun, sunshine!"
Dr. Nefario says as he blasts El Macho in the face with a Fart Gun.

El Macho passes out, finally defeated!

Gru climbs onto the rocket. "I will get you out of this," he reassures Lucy.
Just then, Pollito finds the remote and pecks the button.

"I really hate that chicken," groans Gru as the rocket blasts off.

Gru looks Lucy in the eyes. "Listen, Lucy . . . we may not get out of this alive, so I need to know. If I'd asked you out on a date, what would you have said?"

Lucy smiles. "Yes!" she says happily. They stare at each other for a moment. Gru realises they are about to crash into the volcano. He grabs Lucy's hand and screams, "Jump!" They splash into the water below. After a second, they pop up, spluttering - and in love!

A few months later, Gru and Lucy get married.
Agnes doesn't have to pretend to have a mum anymore. She looks at Lucy and says,

"She kisses my boo-boos.
She braids my hair.
We love you, mothers, everywhere!
But my mom, Lucy, is beyond compare."

Lucy hugs Agnes. Gru, Margo and Edith all join in.
Their family is now complete!

Answers

Page 6

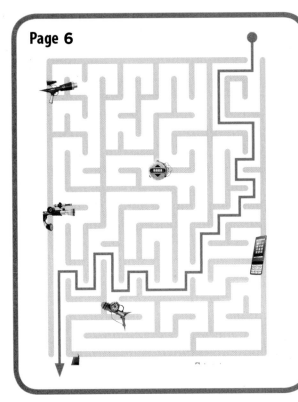

Page 7

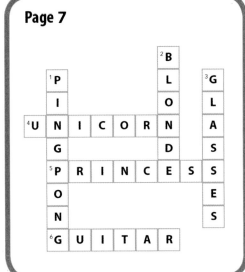

					B				G
P					L				L
I					O				A
U	N	I	C	O	R	N			S
G					D				S
		P	R	I	N	C	E	S	S
O									E
N									S
G	U	I	T	A	R				

Page 11

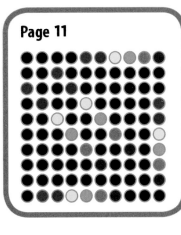

Page 10
Lucy's message reads,
'TOP SECRET: BREAK-IN TONIGHT.'

Page 9

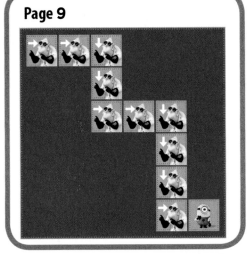

Page 13

Page 8

A	R	O	N	B	P	G	P	A	R	A	D	I	S	E
R	L	K	A	I	E	R	O	L	L	W	A	Q	D	R
Y	P	P	A	H	X	Z	C	B	T	I	G	I	H	Y
A	G	N	E	S	F	S	S	U	Y	T	T	S	O	V
M	A	R	A	M	E	O	A	L	O	H	L	E	V	M
S	S	J	Y	D	V	W	O	N	U	A	O	U	O	S
N	H	N	B	L	T	T	O	D	R	M	I	K	C	N
P	O	B	L	Y	L	M	E	E	C	T	Y	Z	F	T
E	P	E	W	M	A	A	K	E	T	O	H	O	E	K
K	S	A	R	O	E	R	M	N	O	Q	U	L	R	H
A	A	U	T	Y	P	G	O	T	R	N	P	R	E	J
C	T	T	K	P	F	O	L	D	T	L	O	G	T	G
P	F	O	R	N	E	T	I	A	S	K	P	P	D	V
U	O	F	R	V	D	N	I	B	L	A	O	R	A	E
C	O	U	E	A	T	N	A	R	U	A	T	S	E	R

Page 12
Minions 3, 7 and 8 have been given the serum.